bebop jazz

bebop jazz

Arranged by James Sodke

HLE
Hal Leonard Europe
Distributed by Music Sales

Exclusive Distributors:
Music Sales Limited
8/9 Frith Street, London W1D 3JB, England.

Order No. HLE90002253
ISBN 1-84449-734-8

Printed in the USA

Your Guarantee of Quality
As publishers, we strive to produce every book to the highest commercial standards.
The book has been carefully designed to minimise awkward page turns and to make playing from it a real pleasure.
Throughout, the printing and binding have been planned to ensure a sturdy, attractive publication which should give years of enjoyment.
If your copy fails to meet our high standards, please inform us and we will gladly replace it.

www.musicsales.com

contents

ANTHROPOLOGY

By CHARLIE PARKER
and DIZZY GILLESPIE

D.S. al Coda

CODA

AU PRIVAVE

By CHARLIE PARKER

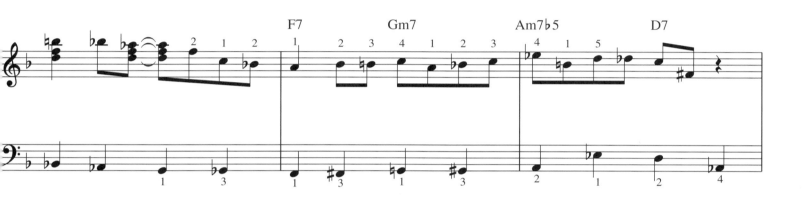

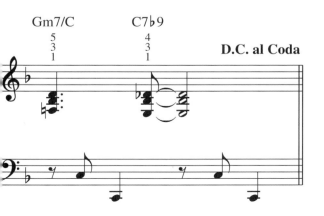

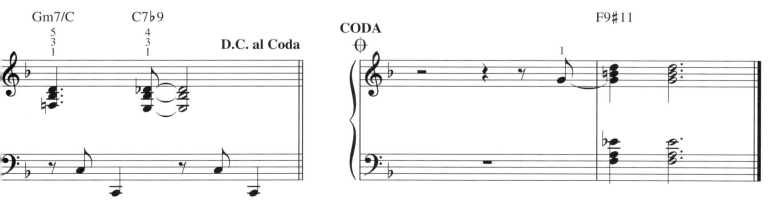

BIRK'S WORKS

By DIZZY GILLESPIE

FOUR

By MILES DAVIS

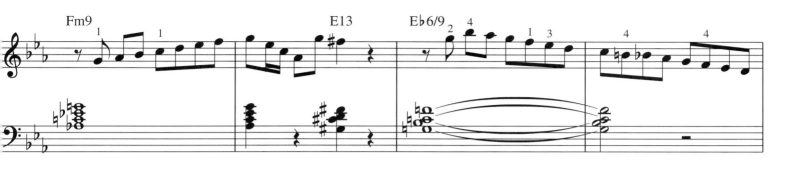

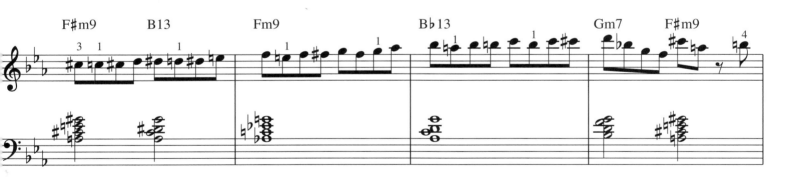

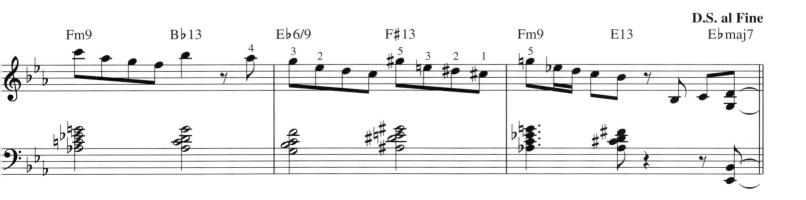

CONFIRMATION

By CHARLIE PARKER

DOXY

By SONNY ROLLIN

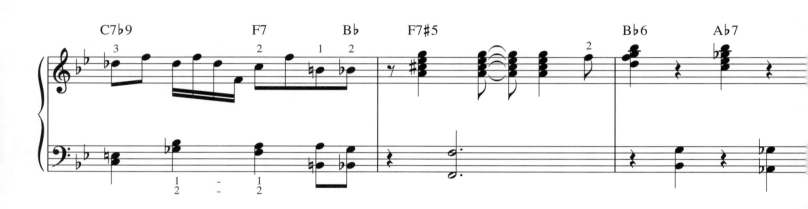

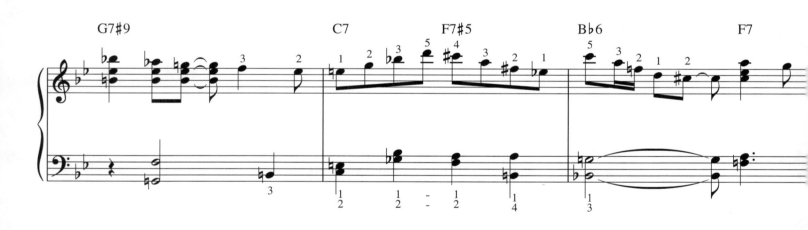

IN WALKED BUD

By THELONIOUS MONK

LEMON DROP

Composed by GEORGE WALLINGTON

LADY BIRD

By TADD DAMERON

MANTECA

By DIZZY GILLESPIE, WALTER GIL FULLER
and LUCIANO POZO GONZALES

Moderate Latin

8vb

SHAWNUFF

By CHARLIE PARKER
and JOHN "DIZZY" GILLESPIE

D.S. al Coda

A NIGHT IN TUNISIA

Music by JOHN "DIZZY" GILLESPIE
and FRANK PAPARELLI

Moderately

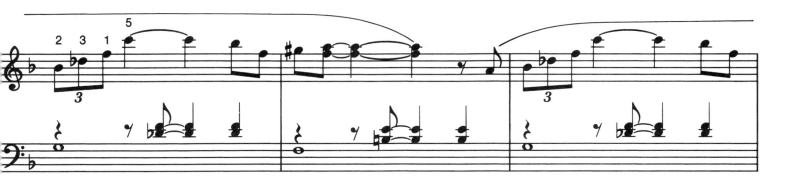

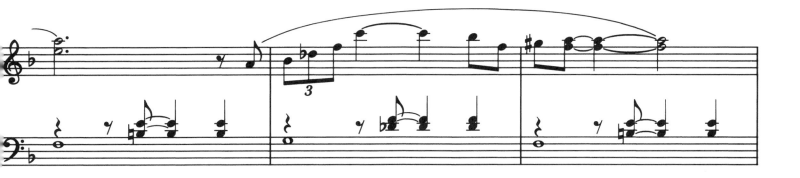

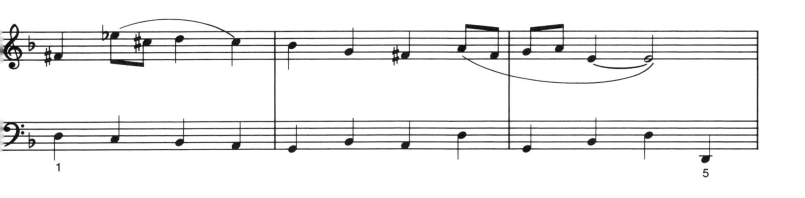

OLEO

By SONNY ROLLINS

ORNITHOLOGY

By CHARLIE PARKER
and BENNIE HARRIS

Moderate Jazz tempo

RUBY, MY DEAR

By THELONIOUS MONK

SALT PEANUTS

Music by JOHN "DIZZY" GILLESPIE
and KENNY CLARKE

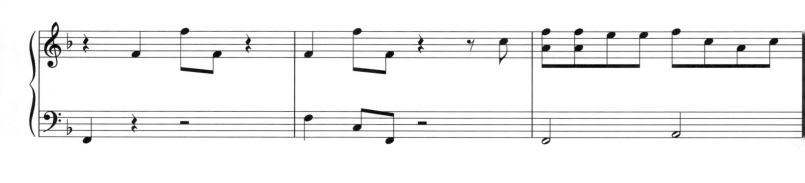

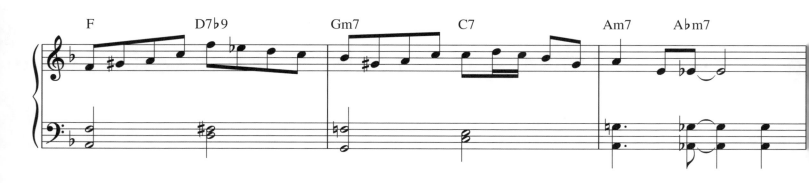

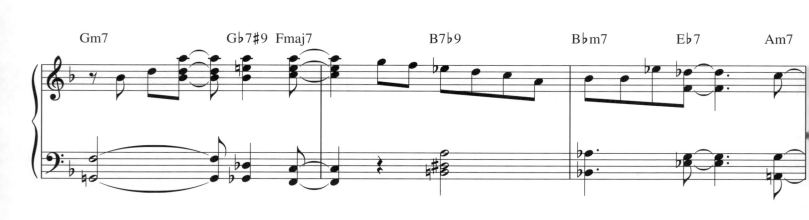

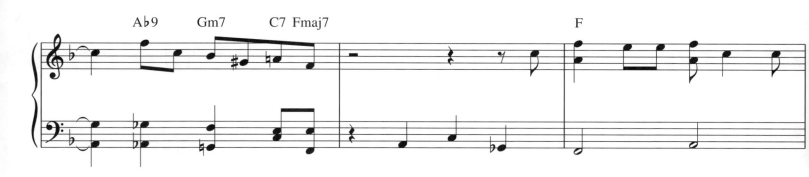

TEMPUS FUGIT

By EARL BUD POWELL

WELL YOU NEEDN'T
(It's Over Now)

English Lyric by MIKE FERRO
Music by THELONIOUS MONK

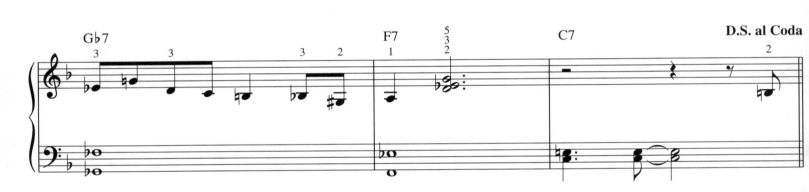